This
Dora the Explorer Annual
belongs to

Contents

EGMONT

We bring stories to life

First published in Great Britain 2012 by Egmont UK Limited
239 Kensington High Street, London W8 6SA

© 2012 Viacom International, Inc.
All rights reserved.
Nickelodeon, Nick Jr., Dora the Explorer and all related titles, logos and characters are trademarks of Viacom International Inc.

Written by Jenny Bak. Designed by Pritty Ramjee and Ant Duke.

ISBN 978 1 4052 6403 7
51956/1
Printed in Italy

Adult supervision is recommended when glue, paint, scissors and other sharp points are in use.

¡Hola, Explorers!

I'm Dora, and this is my best friend, Boots. We love to go exploring all year long.

Do you know the four seasons, **estaciones**, of the year? They're Spring, Summer, Autumn and Winter. Each season gives us fun things to do. Let's find out what they are!

Can you see a mouse, **ratón**, hiding behind the tree? There are 6 more mice hiding in the pages of this annual. Colour in a cheese for every one you spot.

All answers can be found on page 68!

Speak Spanish with Dora! There's a word list on page 66 to help you learn.

Spring Party

Come and meet my family, **mi familia**. This is Mami, Papi and my grandmother, Abuela. And here are my baby brother and sister, Guillermo and Isabella. They're twins!

Mami

Papi

Abuela

Dora

Guillermo

Isabella

The twins' birthday is in the springtime, **primavera**, so we're having a spring dance party! Mami is going to dance with Guillermo, Papi is going to dance with Abuela and I'm going to dance with Isabella. Draw lines to match us up!

Guillermo

Isabella

Mami

Papi

Dora

Abuela

How many birthday presents did the twins receive?

We've decorated the house for the party. What colours are the balloons?

When is your birthday?

Flower Friends

Springtime is when plants and flowers grow. Boots and I are visiting our friends to give them some colourful spring flowers, **flores**.

Let's Go! ¡Vámonos!

Isa

Tico

Dora

10

¡Hola, Isa! I'm going to give Isa some pretty red flowers, **flores rojos**. Colour them in for her!

Tico loves yellow, so he gets the yellow flowers, **flores amarillos**. Colour them in, too.

Swiper

Oh no, there's Swiper! He's going to swipe all the flowers. Say "**Swiper, no swiping!**" three times to stop him.

Benny

Boots

Great! We've stopped Swiper. Now we can give Benny the blue flowers, **flores azules**. Colour them in!

Make a Sunflower

You can make a flower to give, just like Dora.
Ask an adult to help you.

You will need:

- [x] Brown paper or card
- [x] Cup or beaker
- [x] Pencil
- [x] Safety scissors
- [x] Yellow tissue paper
- [x] Glue
- [x] Green drinking straw
- [x] Green tissue paper
- [x] Sticky tape

Whenever you see these scissors, ask an adult to help you with cutting out.

1 Draw around the cup on the brown paper, then cut out the circle.

2 Cut some petal shapes out of the yellow tissue paper.

3 Stick your petals around the edge of the circle with glue to make a sunflower face.

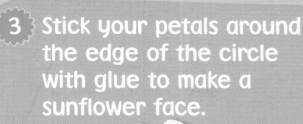

4 Leave to dry. Meanwhile, cut out some leaf shapes from the green paper.

5 Fold the leaves slightly in the middle. Then use sticky tape to stick them on the green straw to make a stem.

6 When the petals are dry, use sticky tape to attach the stem onto the back of the sunflower face.

Have fun with your sunflower!

Baby Animals

Lots of baby animals are born in the spring.
We're going to visit some baby bunnies at the farm.
Which path will take us there?

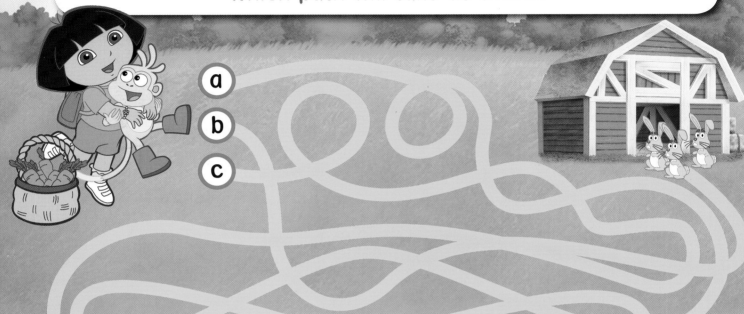

a

b

c

One of these shadows matches this baby lamb.
Which one is it? Tick the box.

1

2

3

4

What animals do the
other shadows belong to?

What Comes Next?

Which farm animal comes next in each row?
Make the animal's sound, then colour it in.

Neigh!   Cluck!   Neigh!   Cluck!   Neigh!

Quack!   Moo!   Quack!   Moo!   Quack!

Baa!   Oink!   Baa!

Dora's New Puppy

¡Hola! I have a new puppy at home. His name is **Perrito**. He's so cute and cuddly. I can't wait to show him to you. Let's go! **¡Vámonos!**

We're passing Abuela's house. Look, there she is! And she has a present, **un regalo**, for Perrito! Let's take it to him right away, before Swiper can swipe it. Will you help us get the gift home quickly? Great!

Map says the quickest way back to my house is through the Butterfly Garden, then past the Ten Dancing Trees. Got it? ¡Bueno! Good!

My Explorer Star tells me that Swiper is going to swipe the gift with a robot butterfly in the Butterfly Garden. It's purple with yellow stripes. Can you find it?

You found it! We'll stay away from that butterfly so it can't swipe Perrito's present.

Where do we go next? That's right, the Ten Dancing Trees.

I see trees, **árboles**, to the left and trees to the right. We need to head towards a group of ten trees.

Can you count the trees?

Colour in the numbers as you count!
1 2 3 4 5
6 7 8 9 10

Great! You found the Ten Dancing Trees, but they're far away. Can you spot someone who can give us a ride?

There's Tico in his car! He can give us a ride over that bridge to the trees.

How many pink birds can you spot?

Oh no, Swiper is chasing us on his fast rocket skates! Tell Tico **"más rápido"** to help him drive faster.

We're going faster! But the bridge is very bumpy, and the car is bouncing a lot. Oh no, the present has bounced into the water!

Will you check Backpack for something to get the present out of the water? Say **Backpack!**

Great! You've found a fishing pole. Now we can get the present out of the river and keep going.

Dancing like a tree is fun!

Tico has brought us to the Ten Dancing Trees. ¡Gracias!

In order to pass, we have to dance like trees. Will you help us?

Stand up tall and straight. Put your arms up in the air like branches and wave them around.

Good dancing!

That present is for Perrito!

Wait. There are supposed to be ten trees, but I see eleven. Oh no, the last tree is really Swiper. He swiped Perrito's present!

Will you ask Swiper for the present nicely? He really loves puppies. Maybe he'll give it back. Say "**Please, Swiper!**" three times.

We did it! Swiper loves puppies so much that he felt bad for swiping Perrito's present and gave it back. Now we're finally home, and there's my puppy. ¡Hola, Perrito!

Let's open the present. What has Abuela has given you? A bowl, a lead and a bone! Perrito is so happy!

Yip! Yip! Yip!

Thanks for helping. ¡Gracias!

Boots loves summertime because we can go to the beach! It's lots of fun to go swimming and build sandcastles in the warm sunshine.

Tico's come to the beach in his boat, **barco**. Can you help us find our way across the sand to his boat? Great!

Avoid the crabs or they'll tickle your toes!

START

Can you spot the sea horse that matches this one?

a   b   c   d

Match Up

Summer is the best time to play sports, **deportes!** Dora is sorting out her summer sports equipment. Draw lines to match them with their shadows.

Colour Dora. Make her shirt yellow.

What sports do you like to play?

Sporty Spanish

Boots and Tico want to play sports together, but Tico only speaks Spanish. Help them learn the names of these sports in English and Spanish. Some names almost sound the same!

tenis

= tennis

Say it like this,
TEN-ees

ciclismo

= cycling

Say it like this,
see-KLEES-mo

voleibol

= volleyball

Say it like this,
VO-lay-boll

A New Game

You can help read this story! When you come to a picture, say the name.

sun

Dora

Boots

tennis

football

goal

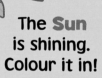

The **Sun** is shining. Colour it in!

The is shining this summer day

 wants to go out and play.

"Let's play ," she says to Boots.

But has a ⚽ and wants to shoot!

28

He's already gone and set up a ,

By putting a net between two poles.

 doesn't know what to do.

They can't play  and  too!

Boots is ready to play! Colour him in!

Boots is about to score a goal. Colour him in!

Then an idea pops into her head.

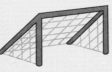 gets racquets and balls from the shed.

"We'll use the racquets to hit the balls in the  to score points," she calls.

Boots says, "It's a  and ⚽ mix!

But we use racquets instead of kicks!"

Dora and Boots love their new game.

Can you see why they picked Footennis

as its name?

Dora is playing footennis. Colour her in!

Going on Holiday

Dora and her friends are on an island holiday for the summer!
Find the five differences between these two pictures.

Colour in a pair of sunglasses for each one you find.

Which Way?

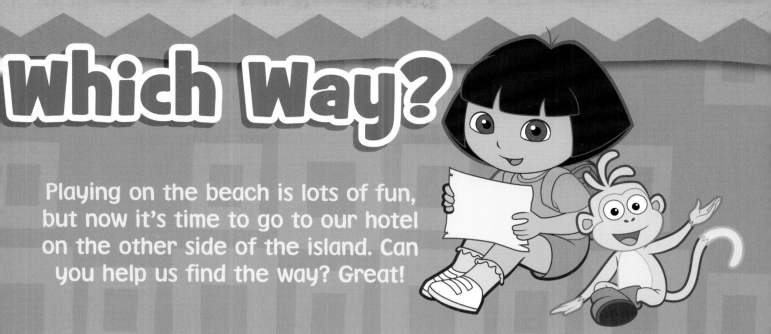

Playing on the beach is lots of fun, but now it's time to go to our hotel on the other side of the island. Can you help us find the way? Great!

START

FINISH

How many ice cream cones did you pass along the way?

Make a Maraca

There's a big party, **fiesta**, on the island.
Let's make a maraca and join in the music!
Ask an adult to help you.

You will need:

- [x] Water bottle
- [x] Masking tape
- [x] Paint
- [x] Paintbrush
- [x] Marker pens
- [x] Paper for funnel
- [x] Uncooked rice

1 Wrap an empty, travel-size water bottle with masking tape, leaving the cap free.

2 Decorate the covered bottle using paint or markers, and let dry.

3 Put two handfuls of uncooked rice into the bottle. A paper funnel makes it easier.

4 Replace the cap tightly, then shake, shake, shake to make some noise, just like Boots!

Island Exploring

This island has lots of colourful bugs.
Can you spot the **orugas**, caterpillars?

Fill this page with bright colours!

How many ladybirds can you spot? Write your answer here, then colour them in!

Colour this butterfly's wings with a stripy pattern!

37

Going Buggy

I found three bugs that look very busy. Starting at the bottom, follow the wiggly lines to find where each bug is going!

How many rabbits are there? Write your answer in the box!

START

Ice Cream Count

Our holiday is almost over, but there's time for one last treat. Here comes an ice cream truck! Count up the different ice creams and lollies, then write the numbers in the boxes below.

Can you guess Boots' ice cream flavour?

Draw a big heart around the one you'd most like to eat!

Autumn Adventures

It's autumn, **otoño**, and the leaves are changing colour.

My friends and I are picking juicy apples and tasty pumpkins.

We love autumn!

What colour are the apples, **manzanas**, in Dora's basket?

How many acorns is Tico holding?

How many rabbits can you count?

Find and tick

41

Back to School

Boots and I are excited for our first day back at **escuela**, school. Will you join us? Great!

Colour Dora and Boots with your brightest colours!

Classroom Hunt

This is my classroom at school. My teacher, Maestra Beatriz, is ready to start her lesson.

What colours are on Dora's school socks?

Colours and Shapes

Maestra Beatriz is teaching us about colours and shapes today. Copy the shapes below onto the whiteboard using the same colours.

Say the name of the shape and colour as you draw them, too!

Lunchtime Puzzle

Mami has made Dora a delicious lunch!
Circle the 5 differences in these two pictures.

Can you spot the five differences between these two pictures?

When you find each difference, colour in a piece of fruit!

School Trip

¡**Hola**, explorers! Maestra Beatriz is taking us to the museum, **museo**. It's very windy as we walk. Draw lines to match the weather words to the pictures they belong with.

wind
viento

sun
sol

rain
lluvia

snow
nieve

Museum Adventures

Let's explore some of the different rooms in the museum.

Planetarium

The planetarium has pictures of the stars and planets in space.

Which planet is the biggest?
Which is the smallest?

Count the stars,
then circle the right number.

1 2 3 4 6 7 8 9 10

Join the dots to finish this picture of a rocket ship.

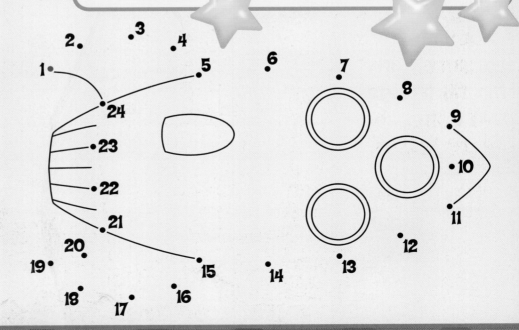

The Gallery

There are many beautiful paintings, **pinturas**, in the gallery. Draw a picture of yourself here.

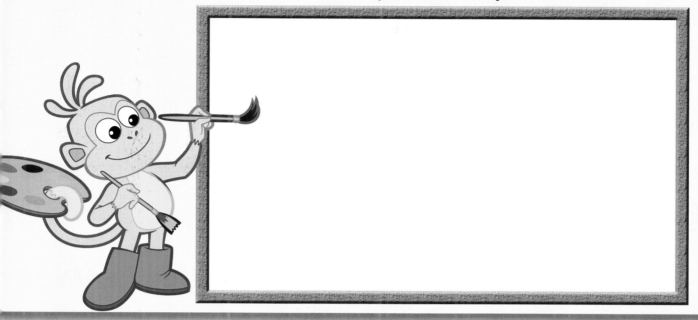

Artefacts Room

The artefacts room holds treasures from a long time ago. Colour in this treasure chest and fill it with gold coins and pretty jewels.

Museum Maze

We're ready to go back to school but Boots is lost in the museum! Help find him by going through all the different rooms.

What has Dora found? Join the dots to find out!

START

Which planet is the one we live on, Earth? Draw a box around it.

Planetarium

Artefacts Room

Gallery

How many pieces of old treasure can you find?

FINISH

Library Visit

On the way home, Boots and I are going to visit the **biblioteca**, library. I want to read a book about dogs. What do you like to read about?

LIBRARY CARD

Dora

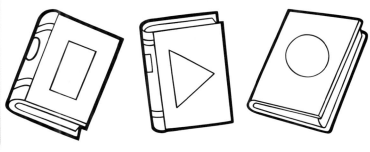

I need a library card to borrow books from the library.
Trace over the grey lines to draw my picture on the card, then colour in the books!

51

How many carved pumpkins can you see? Write the number here

Finish the castle decorations by colouring in the bunting and balloons.

Colour in Boots' bird costume with your favourite colours!

TRICK 'N TREAT

53

Winter Wonderland

Wintertime, **el invierno**, is a special season because it brings snow and Christmas! It's cold outside, so we have to dress in warm winter clothes. Circle the odd one out in each picture.

A Present for Santa

¡Hola!
It's Christmas Eve and
Boots has come for a sleepover!
I have a present, *regalo*, for Boots
under the tree already. It has stars
on it. Can you point to it?

Great!
We're waiting
for Santa so we can
give him a present, too.
It has his picture on it.
What colour is
his present?

My present for
Dora has rainbows on it.
Can you find that one?

Oh no, we fell asleep and missed Santa! We've got to give him his present. Do you know where he lives?

That's right, the North Pole! Map will show us the way. Say "Map"!

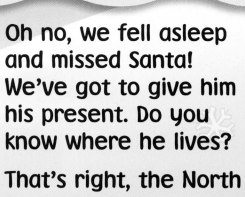

Map says we need to go up the Snowy Mountains, then cross the Icy River to get to the North Pole. Let's ask our train friend, Azul, for a ride to the Snowy Mountains!

Azul means blue in Spanish. Point to the train you think is Azul.

Azul is bringing us to the Snowy Mountains.
We'll pass Tico, Isa and Benny along the way.
Can you see them? What are they doing?

What is the snowman wearing?

Oh no, Santa's present has fallen in the
snow. We can find it by its shape,
a rectangle. Can you spot a rectangle
shape in the snow? What are the
other shapes you can see?

The train tracks have ended, so let's say goodbye to Azul. **¡Adios!** Can you wave goodbye to him, too?

Now we need to find a way to go down the mountain, but it's very snowy. I bet Backpack has something that can help us.

Say "BACKPACK"!

Great! Which of these things can help us travel through snow? Colour it your favourite colour.

We've used the skis to reach the Icy River. Look, there's a puppy in trouble. He needs to cross the river to join his mum and dad, but it's too wide.

Let's look around for help. I see bunnies, polar bears and whales. Which animal lives in the water and can help us get across the river? Point to the right one.

Right, the whales can help us. We'll jump along their backs to cross the river.

NORTH POLE

We made it across the Icy River! Where do we go next?

The North Pole!

Can you see a sign for the North Pole?

The dogs kindly brought us to the North Pole on a sledge. Gracias, perros!

Here's Santa back from delivering presents to all the boys and girls.

Let's give him our present now. It's a guitar, una guitarra, to play music!

Now, count the reindeer, then colour in Santa's sleigh.

Snowy Maze

Dora and Boots are going back to the North Pole to sing carols to Santa. Trace their path to his house in this snowy maze!

START

FINISH

How many gifts did you pick up along the way?

Santa's Reindeer

You can leave a gift for Santa, too! Ask an adult to help you make a reindeer, then leave it for Santa on Christmas Eve.

1

Cut out a triangle shape with round corners out of brown paper, as big as an adult's hand. This will be the reindeer's head.

2

Place your hands on black paper and trace around them with a pencil to make the antlers. Carefully cut them out then glue them to the back of the head.

3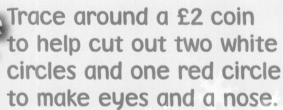

Trace around a £2 coin to help cut out two white circles and one red circle to make eyes and a nose.

4

Colour in a small black circle in each of the white circles as shown here.

5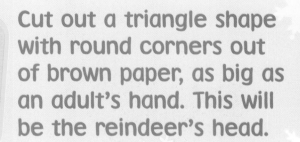

Glue the circles onto the reindeer head to make his friendly face.

Happy Christmas!

It's Christmas morning, and Dora and Boots are opening their presents. ¡Feliz Navidad!

How many candy canes can you count in the picture?

Colour in the objects below when you find them in the big picture.

Spanish Word List

ENGLISH	SPANISH	SAY
Hello	Hola	say OH-la
seasons	estaciones	say es-ta-see-OH-nez
mouse	ratón	say ra-TOHN
my family	mi familia	say ME fa-MIL-li-ah
springtime	primavera	say pree-ma-VEH-ra
let's go	vámonos	say VAH-mo-nos
flowers	flores	say FLOH-rez
red	rojo	say RO-ho
yellow	amarillo	say ah-ma-REE-yo
blue	azul	say ah-SOOL
present	regalo	say reh-GAH-lo
good	bueno	say BWAY-no
trees	árboles	say AR-boh-lez
faster	más rápido	say MAHS RA-pee-doh
thank you	gracias	say GRAH-see-ahs
boat	barco	say BAR-ko
summer	verano	say vehr-AH-no
sports	deportes	say deh-POHR-tez

English	Spanish	Pronunciation
tennis	tenis	say TEN-ees
cycling	ciclismo	say see-KLEES-moh
volleyball	voleibol	say VO-lay-boll
party	fiesta	say fee-ES-ta
caterpillar	oruga	say oh-ROO-ga
autumn	otoño	say oh-TOHN-yo
apple	manzana	say mahn-ZA-na
school	escuela	say es-KWAY-la
very good	muy bien	say MWEE bee-EHN
teacher	maestra	say my-AY-stra
museum	museo	say moo-SAY-oh
wind	viento	say vee-EHN-toh
sun	sol	say SOHL
rain	lluvia	say YOO-vee-ah
snow	nieve	say nee-EH-veh
painting	pintura	say pin-TOO-ra
library	biblioteco	say bib-lee-oh-TEH-ka
winter	invierno	say in-vee-AIR-no
goodbye	adiós	say ah-dee-OHS
guitar	guitarra	say ghee-TA-ra
Happy Christmas!	¡Feliz Navidad!	say feh-LEES na-vee-DAHD

Answers

Page 7

The mice are hiding on pages **11**, **20**, **29**, **40**, **52** and **61**.

Page 9

There are **3** presents. The balloons are **yellow**, **green** and **red**.

Page 14

Path **b** leads to the farm.
Shadow **2** matches the lamb.
Shadow **1** is a pig, shadow **3** is a chicken, shadow **4** is a cow.

Pages 24-25

Picture **d** matches the sea horse. The **rubber ring, bucket** and **spade** should be taken to the beach. There are **6** shells.

Page 26

Page 32

Page 33

There are **6** ice cream cones.

Page 38

The ladybird is going to the rock, the bee is going to the flowers and the butterfly is going to the bush.

Page 39

There are **8** chocolate ice creams, **9** purple lollies, **4** green lollies and **6** red lollies.

Pages 40-41

Page 43

Dora needs pencils, books, a ruler, crayons and an apple for the teacher! She has 2 red pencils and 3 blue books.

Pages 44-45

Page 46

Page 47

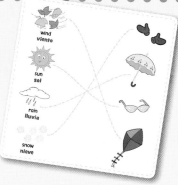

Page 48

Planet **c** is the biggest. Planet **a** is the smallest. There are **8** stars.

Page 50

Dora's found a vase.

Page 54

The scarf, earmuffs and welly boot are the odd ones out.

Page 62

Page 64-65